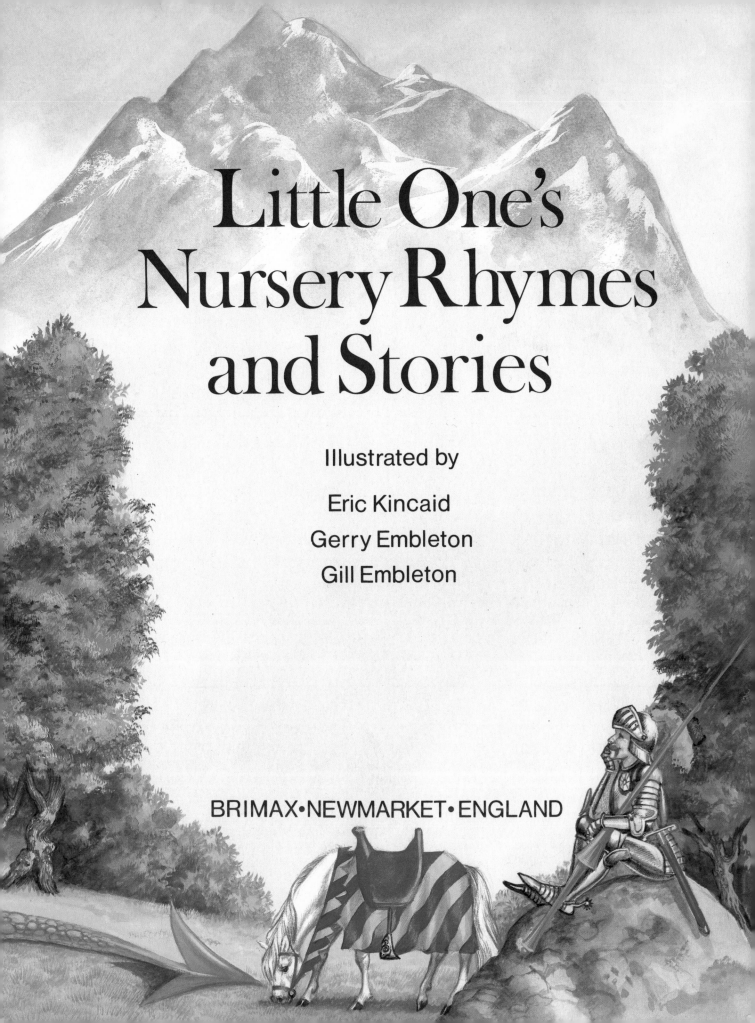

Little One's Nursery Rhymes and Stories

Illustrated by

Eric Kincaid

Gerry Embleton

Gill Embleton

BRIMAX·NEWMARKET·ENGLAND

Contents

NURSERY RHYMES

NURSERY STORIES

ISBN 0 86112 199 6
© BRIMAX RIGHTS LTD 1983 All rights reserved
Published by BRIMAX BOOKS, NEWMARKET, ENGLAND 1983
Second Printing 1984
Some of the rhymes, stories and illustrations in
this collection appear in TREASURY OF NURSERY
RHYMES and others in OMNIBUS OF FAIRY TALES
published by BRIMAX BOOKS
Printed in Hong Kong

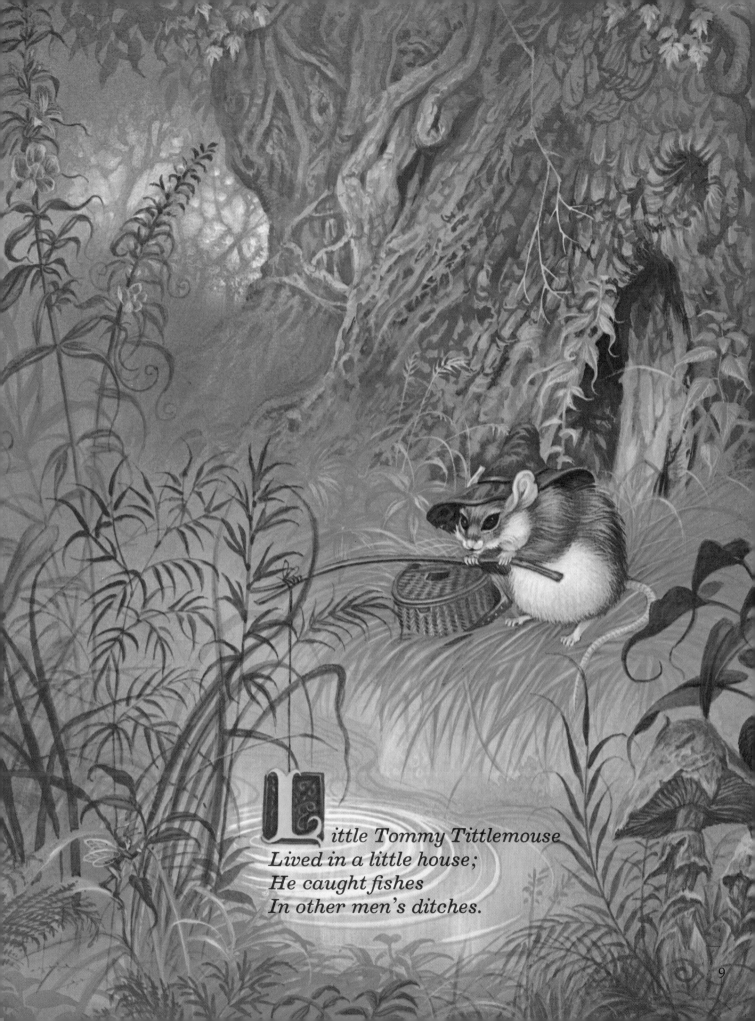

Little Tommy Tittlemouse
Lived in a little house;
He caught fishes
In other men's ditches.

Three young rats with black felt hats,
Three young ducks with white straw flats,
Three young dogs with curling tails,
Three young cats with demi-veils,
Went out to walk with two young pigs
In satin vests and sorrel wigs.
But suddenly it chanced to rain
And so they all went home again.

Pussy cat Mole jumped over a coal
And in her best petticoat burnt a great hole.
Poor pussy's weeping, she'll have no more milk
Until her best petticoat's mended with silk.

11

Little Bo-peep has lost her sheep,
And can't tell where to find them;
Leave them alone, and they'll come home,
And bring their tails behind them.

Little Bo-peep fell fast asleep,
And dreamt she heard them bleating;
But when she awoke, she found it a joke,
For they were still all fleeting.

Then up she took her little crook,
Determined for to find them;
She found them indeed, but it made her heart bleed,
For they'd left their tails behind them.

12

It happened one day, as Bo-peep did stray
Into a meadow hard by,
There she espied their tails side by side,
All hung on a tree to dry.

She heaved a sigh, and wiped her eye,
And over the hillocks went rambling,
And tried what she could, as a shepherdess should,
To tack again each to its lambkin.

The Gingerbread Man

A little old man and a little old woman lived in a tiny cottage. Every day was the same, because they had no children to play with or to make them laugh.

One day, the little old woman had an idea. It was such a splendid idea, she had to sit down and think about it. The little old man was sitting outside in the sun, so the little old woman said to herself,

"I will make a little gingerbread man!"

She started mixing things, fat, sugar, and eggs; then flour and ginger. She put in lots of ginger and made him a lovely dark brown. She rolled the dough and cut out the shape of a little man.

"Now, currants for his eyes and his buttons. Some lemon peel for his nose and his mouth. . . . That's fine!"

She slid the gingerbread onto a baking sheet and put it into the oven to bake.

Later that morning, the little old woman heard a voice,

"Let me out!. . . . Let me out!"

The voice came from the oven!
Very carefully, she peeped inside.
The Gingerbread Man leapt out!
"Wait!" she called. "Come
back!" But he was off and
running fast.
"Don't just sit there, little
old man!" she cried. "Help me
catch him!"

They ran after him.
"Stop! . . . Stop!" they shouted.
The Gingerbread Man grinned
and called,
"Run, run as fast as you can
You can't catch me
I'm the Gingerbread Man."
And they couldn't!
A cow stood across his path. The Gingerbread Man ran
between its legs.
"Mmm-ind your manners!" she mooed. "What are you doing?"
"I am running away!" laughed Gingerbread Man. "I have
run away from the little old woman and the little old man, so
I am running away from you!
Run, run as fast as you can
You can't catch me
I'm the Gingerbread Man."
He was right. The cow could not catch him!

He raced past a horse trotting through a gate.

"Whoa!" called the horse. "Wait for me!"

"Are you running away too?" cried the Gingerbread Man.

"Why not? . . . Hee-hee-ee!" neighed the horse. "The gate's open."

"I run away from everybody!" said the Gingerbread Man. "I will run away from you too!

Run, run as fast as you can
You can't catch me
I'm the Gingerbread Man."

And even at a gallop the horse couldn't catch him.

Round the next bend he met a fox.

"Hallo!" called the fox. "Why, you are brown, just like me. . . . Look, we make a good pair."

The Gingerbread Man didn't stop. He ran faster and faster, calling out,

"I've run away from the little old woman, the little old man, a cow AND a horse, so I can run away from you!

Run, run as fast as you can
You can't catch me
I'm the Gingerbread Man."

But . . .

At last he stopped on the edge of a river.

"Oh!" said the Gingerbread Man, "I shall get wet . . . What can I do?"

Up came the fox.

"You can sit on my tail, little brown friend. We will cross the river in no time."

So the Gingerbread Man climbed onto the fox's tail.

Soon the fox said, "Little friend, you will get wet on my tail. Jump on my back."

So the Gingerbread Man jumped onto the fox's back.

Half-way across the river the fox said, "Little friend, you are too heavy. Jump on my nose . . . You will be able to see better."

The Gingerbread Man laughed and jumped onto the fox's nose.

"This is fun!" he said.

When the fox had nearly reached the other side, he tossed his head. Up went the Gingerbread Man, spinning over and over in the air. Then . . . snap! snap! He was caught!

The fox gobbled him up and that was the end of the Gingerbread Man.

There was a crooked man, and he walked a crooked mile,
He found a crooked sixpence against a crooked stile;
He bought a crooked cat,
                        which caught a crooked mouse,
            And they all lived together in a little crooked house.

There was an old woman who lived in a shoe,
She had so many children she didn't know what to do;
She gave them some broth without any bread;
She whipped them all soundly and put them to bed.

Ladybird, ladybird,
Fly away home,
Your house is on fire
And your children all gone;
All except one
And that's little Ann
And she has crept under
The warming pan.

Ding, dong, bell,
Pussy's in the well.
Who put her in?
Little Johnny Green.
Who pulled her out?
Little Tommy Stout.
What a naughty boy was that,
To try to drown poor pussy cat,
Who never did him any harm,
And killed the mice in his father's barn.

Hey diddle diddle,
The cat and the fiddle,
The cow jumped over the moon,
The little dog laughed
To see such sport,
And the dish ran away with the spoon.

Higglety, pigglety, pop!
The dog has eaten the mop;
The pig's in a hurry,
The cat's in a flurry,
Higglety, pigglety, pop!

Sing a song of sixpence,
A pocket full of rye;
Four and twenty blackbirds,
Baked in a pie.

When the pie was opened,
The birds began to sing;
Was not that a dainty dish,
To set before the king?

The king was in his counting house,
Counting out his money;
The queen was in the parlour,
Eating bread and honey.

The maid was in the garden,
Hanging out the clothes,
There came a little blackbird,
And snapped off her nose.

Little Red Riding Hood

Red Riding Hood lived with her mother in a little cottage on the edge of a wood. Her grandmother lived on the other side of the wood.

One day her mother gave Red Riding Hood a basket of nice things to eat, butter, honey and new-laid eggs.

"Take these to Grandma," said her mother. "She is not well. Keep to the path now. Give Grandma my love and then come home."

"I will," said Red Riding Hood. She waved goodbye.

It was a lovely sunny morning. Red Riding Hood was humming to herself as she came to the wood. She looked very pretty in her red hood and cloak. The birds peeped through the leaves to see her pass. The robin even sang a song for her. A squirrel at the top of a tree, stopped nibbling a nut – just to watch her.

23

When Red Riding Hood came to the middle of the wood, she stopped to pick some flowers. A wolf came along the path to meet her.

"Good morning, my dear," he said. "Where are you going?"

"I am going to see my Grandma," said Red Riding Hood. "She is not well."

"Oh dear," said the wolf kindly, "I am sorry. Have you far to go?"

"Just to the cottage at the end of this path," said Red Riding Hood.

"Well," said the wolf, "I'll say good-day; I am going down this way. I hope your Grandma feels better soon . . . Goodbye!"

Red Riding Hood went on her way, but the wolf did not keep to his path. He turned round and ran along another one to get to Grandma's cottage first.

Grandma saw him coming, and hid under her bed. Her nightcap fell onto the floor.

In came the wolf. He put the nightcap on and climbed into bed.

When Red Riding Hood came to the cottage door, she lifted the latch and walked in. She went over to her Grandma's bed and sat down.

"Look, Grandma, I've brought you lots of nice things to eat . . . Shall I put them in the cupboard?" There was no answer.

When Red Riding Hood turned towards Grandma again, two staring eyes, under a nightcap, watched her from the pillow. The frilly nightcap had slipped and she could see one large ear. 'How Grandma has changed,' thought Red Riding Hood.

"Oh, Grandma," she whispered, "what big ears you have!"

"All the better to hear you with, my dear," said the wolf. How strange Grandma sounded.

"Oh, Grandma, what big eyes you have!"

"All the better to see you with, my dear," said the wolf with a smile.

"Oh, Grandma," said Red Riding Hood, "what big teeth you have!"

"All the better to EAT you with!" said the wolf. He leapt out of the bed, and tried to catch her.

Red Riding Hood screamed. She ran as fast as she could out of the house and down the path into the wood.

Two woodcutters were busy cutting down trees. They heard Red Riding Hood calling for help. At once, they left their work and chased the wolf.

How he ran when he saw the men coming after him! How funny he looked with Grandma's frilly nightcap flapping up and down on one ear! They all watched until the wolf had gone. He was never seen again.

Red Riding Hood was so glad. "Will you help me to find my Grandma, please?" she asked her woodcutter friends.

"Of course we will," they said. Then hand in hand, they all went back to Grandma's cottage.

They looked everywhere for Grandma, but could not find her. They were not looking in the right place, were they?

"Grandma!" called Red Riding Hood. "Where are you? . . ."

"I am here!" said a small voice, and then came a big sneeze. "A . . . TISHOO!"

The frill round the bottom of the bed shook. Red Riding Hood lifted it up to peep underneath. There was Grandma, safe and sound.

"Oh, Grandma!" she cried. "How clever you are!"

When Grandma was back in her bed, Red Riding Hood found her a clean nightcap. They were very happy – all laughing and talking together.

"I feel better," said Grandma. "Let's have a party!"

And they did . . . Lovely brown eggs, with fresh bread and butter, and golden honey.

One woodcutter went to fetch Red Riding Hood's mother. They all had a happy time. The squirrel sprang from branch to branch and all the birds sang louder and louder.

See-saw, Margery Daw,
Jacky shall have a new master;
Jacky shall have but a penny a day,
Because he can't work any faster.

Of all the gay birds that e'er I did see,
The owl is the fairest by far to me,
For all day long she sits on a tree,
And when the night comes away flies she.

There was a little girl, and she had a little curl
Right in the middle of her forehead;
When she was good, she was very, very good,
But when she was bad, she was horrid.

ickety, pickety, my black hen,
She lays eggs for gentlemen;
Gentlemen come every day
To see what my black hen doth lay.
Sometimes nine and sometimes ten,
Hickety, pickety, my black hen.

The Three Billy~Goats Gruff

Once upon a time and far, far away in a land of beautiful mountains, fine green fields and sparkling streams, there lived three billy-goats. They were all named Gruff.

The eldest and largest was called Big Billy-Goat Gruff; the next was called Middle Billy-Goat Gruff; and the youngest and smallest was called Tiny Billy-Goat Gruff.

They had eaten all the grass in their field; they were hungry and getting thinner every day. So, they set off to find a better place, where they could eat and grow fat.

In the distance, on the other side of a wide stream, they saw a fine green field. The grass was thick and long; it was just what they wanted.

"We would get fat on that," said Tiny Billy-Goat Gruff in his little voice.

"Oh yes, we would," added Middle Billy-Goat Gruff in his soft voice.

"Then we must go at once," said Big Billy-Goat Gruff in his loud voice.

Over the stream was a wooden bridge to be crossed and under the bridge lived a troll. Now, a troll is a bad-tempered, ugly dwarf, who has big eyes and a long nose. He likes nothing better than eating goat for his supper. The children who lived in a village nearby, stayed well away from the wooden bridge. Everyone was afraid of the ugly troll.

The three billy-goats looked at the bridge.

"What about the Troll?" asked Tiny Billy-Goat Gruff in his little voice.

"Yes, what about the Troll?" added Middle Billy-Goat Gruff in his soft voice.

"I have a plan," declared Big Billy-Goat Gruff in his loud voice. "Listen carefully." The three goats put their heads close together and they whispered to one another.

Tiny Billy-Goat Gruff was the first to reach the bridge. Trip, trip, trip . . . went his tiny hooves on the wooden boards.

Out came the ugly Troll.

"Who is that?" he roared. "Who is that tripping over my bridge?"

"Oh!" cried Tiny Billy-Goat Gruff in his little voice. "I am Tiny, the smallest Billy-Goat Gruff. I am going to that field over there to eat and grow fat."

"Ha!" roared the Troll again. "No, you are not! I am going to eat YOU!"

Poor Tiny Goat began to shake. He trembled all over.

"Oh, no! Do not bother with me . . . I am very small and I am so thin. Why not wait for the next Billy-Goat Gruff, he is much bigger and fatter."

The ugly Troll stopped to think.

"Very well!" he shouted. "Be off with you!"

So Tiny Billy-Goat Gruff quickly tripped over the bridge and into the fine green field.

Before long, up came Middle Billy-Goat Gruff. Trip, trot, trip, trot . . . went his hooves on the wooden boards.

Out came the ugly Troll.

"Who is that?" he roared. "Who is that trotting over my bridge?"

"Oh!" cried Middle Billy-Goat Gruff in his soft voice. "I am Middle, the second Billy-Goat Gruff. I am on my way to the field over there to eat and grow fat."

"Ha!" roared the Troll again. "No, you are not! I am going to eat YOU!"

Poor Middle Goat began to shake. He trembled all over.

"Oh, no! Do not bother with me . . . I am middle-sized and really quite thin. Why not wait for Big Billy-Goat Gruff; he is really big and very much fatter."

The ugly Troll stopped to think.

"Very well!" he shouted. "Be off with you!"

So Middle Billy-Goat Gruff quickly trotted over the bridge and into the fine green field.

Then came Big Billy-Goat Gruff. Trip, trot, tramp! Trip, trot, tramp . . . went his big hooves on the wooden boards.

Out came the ugly Troll.

"Who is that?" he roared louder than ever. "Who is that tramping over my bridge?"

"Ah!" replied Big Billy-Goat Gruff in his loudest voice. "I am Big, the biggest Billy-Goat Gruff . . . and I am tramping over this bridge!"

The ugly Troll roared with anger. "I am coming to get you," he shouted. He moved a few steps towards the goat.

"Oh, no, you are not!" bellowed Big Billy-Goat Gruff. "I am coming to get YOU!"

He lowered his head and stamped his hooves. Tramp, tramp, TRAMP! Tramp, tramp, TRAMP!

They met in the middle of the bridge and a battle began.

Big Billy-Goat Gruff prodded the ugly Troll with his sharp horns. He picked him up and tossed him into the air. The ugly Troll turned three somersaults before he fell with a splash into the deep water of the stream. He was never seen again.

So Big Billy-Goat Gruff tramped happily across the bridge and into the fine green field. All three billy-goats ate the sweet grass and grew fatter and fatter.

The children in the village were happy. They could use the bridge and play in the fields, for the ugly old Troll was gone forever.

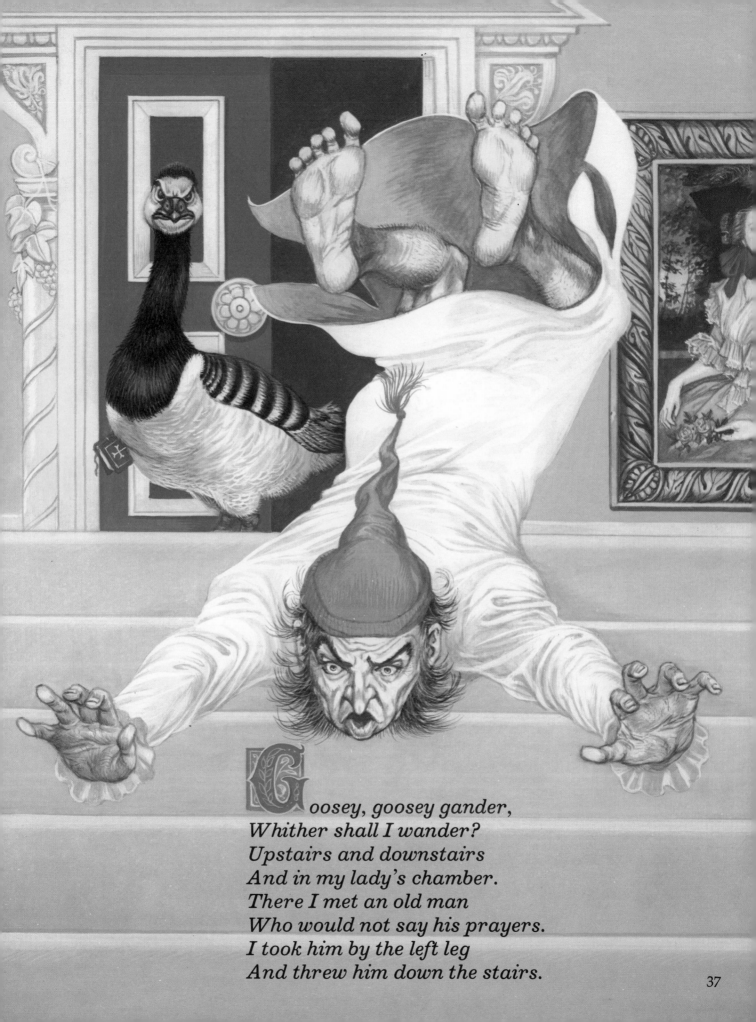

Goosey, goosey gander,
Whither shall I wander?
Upstairs and downstairs
And in my lady's chamber.
There I met an old man
Who would not say his prayers.
I took him by the left leg
And threw him down the stairs.

37

Ring-a-ring o' roses,
A pocket full of posies,
A-tishoo! A-tishoo!
We all fall down.

38

olly put the kettle on,
Polly put the kettle on,
Polly put the kettle on,
We'll all have tea.

Sukey take it off again,
Sukey take it off again,
Sukey take it off again,
They've all gone away.

Little Jack Horner
Sat in the corner,
Eating a Christmas pie;
He put in his thumb,
And pulled out a plum,
And said, What a good boy am I!

Baa, baa, black sheep,
Have you any wool?
Yes, sir, yes, sir,
Three bags full;
One for the master,
And one for the dame,
And one for the little boy
Who lives down the lane.

Rumpelstiltskin

Once there was a miller who had a beautiful daughter. He was always talking about her and saying how clever she was.

One day, the miller had to take some flour to the palace. He told the king about his daughter.

"Her hair is like spun gold, Your Majesty, and what is more, she is so clever she can spin straw into gold."

This was not true. The miller's daughter had never even spun cloth but the king did not know this.

"Bring your daughter to me!" said the king.

The miller almost danced down the steps of the palace. He took his daughter to see the king the very next day.

The king led her into a room where there was a pile of straw, a stool and a spinning wheel.

"Now," said the king. "You must spin this straw into gold by dawn tomorrow or you shall die."

He left the room and locked the door.

The miller's daughter could not understand. How could she spin straw into gold? How could she spin anything? She did not even know how to begin. She crept into a corner of the room and burst into tears.

Suddenly, there was a puff of smoke and a strange little man stood beside her. His face was brown and wrinkled, his nose was long and his white beard almost reached his knobbly knees.

"What's the matter?" he said. "Why are you crying?"

"Whatever shall I do?" the girl said tearfully. "Look at all this straw! The king has said I must spin it into gold by early morning or I shall die! I cannot even spin!"

"Dry your tears," said the little man. "What will you give me if I spin it for you?"

The girl's fingers touched the necklace she was wearing.

"I will give you my necklace," she said.

The strange little man clapped his hands with delight. He sat down to spin. The spinning wheel whirled around. It made a gentle humming sound. The girl's eyes closed and she fell asleep.

While she slept, the straw became a pile of gold. She awoke; the strange little man had vanished.

In the morning, the king could not believe his eyes. A heap of shining gold! "Come with me," he said at once. The king led the girl into a much larger room, which was filled with even more straw. He told her she must spin it into gold by the next day.

Once again the door was locked and the poor girl began to cry. Once more there was a puff of smoke and there stood the strange little man.

"What will you give me this time if I spin the straw?" he asked.

"Oh, thank you, thank you," she said. "I will give you the ring my mother gave me." She slipped the ring off her finger and held it out to him. Without another word, he took it and started to spin.

The next day, although the king was delighted with the gold, he was not satisfied. He took the miller's daughter into a larger room with heaps of straw which nearly reached the ceiling.

"Now, my dear," he said. "Spin all this straw into gold tonight and I will make you my queen."

This time, the girl was very frightened. She knew that if the little man appeared, she had nothing left to give him.

Once again there was a puff of smoke and there he stood. As if he knew already, the strange little man said,

"Promise me that when you are queen, you will give me your first baby. If you promise, I will spin the straw for you."

'How can I promise?' she thought. 'I may never be queen . . . or have a child . . . but it's the only way to get the spinning done.'

"I promise," she whispered.

The strange little man spun the straw into gold and vanished as before.

Next day, the king kept his word. He married the miller's daughter and she became queen.

Some years later, the queen sat smiling at her first baby.
A voice behind her said,

   "Remember your promise? I have come for the child." It
was the strange little man.

   "Oh, no! Do not make me give you my baby!" she begged.
"Take all my other treasure, but let me keep him! Please,
please!"

   "I will give you one chance," he said. "You have three
days in which to tell me my name. If you find my right name,
you may keep the child."

The queen wrote down every name she could think of and sent her servants out to find new names.

"Is it William? . . . David? . . . Rupert?" she asked, when the little man came the next day. To each one he replied, "That is not my name."

On the second day, she tried funny names like Cross-Patch, Double-Dutch and Hanky-Panky, but still he replied,

"That is not my name."

On the third morning, a servant rushed in to see the queen.

"Your Majesty!" he said, "I was in the forest . . . there was a little hut with a fire outside. A strange little man was hopping round it and singing!"

"What was he singing?" asked the queen.

"He sang something like this, Your Majesty . . .

'I will dance and I will sing
Tomorrow will the baby bring
The queen she cannot spoil my game
For Rumpelstiltskin is my name!'

The queen was so happy when she heard this. She gave the servant a bag of gold.

When the strange little man came, he asked,

"Well, my lady, what is my name?"

"James, perhaps?" said the queen. "Richard?"

"No, no," replied the strange little man.

"Rumpelstiltskin then?" said the queen slowly.

The strange little man howled with rage and stamped so hard that his foot sank right through the floor.

"Who told you my name? A witch? Yes, a witch!" he shouted. With a great puff of smoke and in a flash the strange little man was gone. No one ever saw him again.

Two little dicky birds,
Sitting on a wall;
One named Peter,
The other named Paul.

Fly away, Peter!
Fly away, Paul!

Come back, Peter!
Come back, Paul!

48

One, two,
Buckle my shoe;
Three, four,
Knock at the door;
Five, six,
Pick up sticks;
Seven, eight,
Lay them straight;
Nine, ten,
A big fat hen;
Eleven, twelve,
Dig and delve;
Thirteen, fourteen,
Maids a-courting;
Fifteen, sixteen,
Maids in the kitchen;
Seventeen, eighteen,
Maids in waiting;
Nineteen, twenty,
My plate's empty.

Cock a doodle doo!
My dame has lost her shoe,
My master's lost his fiddlestick,
And knows not what to do.

50

Goldilocks and the Three Bears

Once there were three bears. A father bear, a mother bear and a baby bear.

One morning Mother Bear made the porridge for breakfast as usual. "The porridge is exceedingly hot this morning," said Mother Bear.

"Let us go for a stroll in the wood while it cools," said Father Bear.

There was someone else walking in the wood that morning. A little girl with long golden hair, called Goldilocks. She could smell the beautiful aroma of porridge and she followed it, her nose twitching, until she came to the open window of the Bears' house. When she saw the three bowls of steaming porridge on the table they made her feel so hungry she climbed in through the window without so much as a 'please may I?'

"I think I'll try some of that," she said. She tried the porridge in the large bowl first. It was so hot it burnt her tongue.

"Ouch!" she said, and dropped the spoon.

The porridge in the middle size bowl was far too sweet.

"Ugh!" she said, and dropped that spoon too.

The porridge in the small bowl was just the way she liked it.

"Ooh lovely!" she said, and ate it all up.

When the small bowl was quite, quite empty she walked around the house opening cupboards, and looking at this, and looking at that, and trying everything she could see.

She sat on Father Bear's big chair.

"Oh no . . ." she said, "This is much too hard."

She sat on Mother Bear's middle size chair.

"Oh no . . ." she said, "This is much too soft."

She sat on Baby Bear's chair.

"Ooh lovely!" she said. "This is so comfortable."

But she wriggled and fidgeted about so much that one of the legs snapped in two and she fell to the floor.

She picked herself up and went into the bear's bedroom.

She tried Father Bear's big bed.

"Oh no . . ." she said. "This is much too bumpy."

She tried Mother Bear's middle size bed.

"Oh no . . ." she said, "This is much too squashy."

She tried Baby Bear's small bed.

"Ooh lovely!" she said, "This is so comfortable." And she fell fast asleep with her head on Baby Bear's pillow.

When the bears got home they could tell at once that someone had been inside their house.

"Who has been eating my porridge?" growled Father Bear.

"Who has been eating my porridge?" growled Mother Bear.

"And who has been eating my porridge, and finished it all up?" squeaked Baby Bear.

"Who has been sitting on my chair?" growled Father Bear.

"Who has been sitting on my chair?" growled Mother Bear.

"And who has been sitting on my chair, and broken it?" squeaked Baby Bear and he burst into tears.

"Who has been lying on my bed?" growled Father Bear.
"Who has been lying on my bed?" growled Mother Bear.
"Someone has been lying on my bed and she is still here."
squeaked Baby Bear. "LOOK!"

Goldilocks opened her eyes and sat up. When she saw the
three bears staring at her she jumped off the bed and out through
the window so quickly the bears were taken by surprise.

The bears didn't bother to chase after her. She looked so
frightened they knew she had learned her lesson and would never
go uninvited into someone else's house again.

Instead, Mother Bear made some more porridge for Baby
Bear. Father Bear mended his chair. And then they all sat down
and had breakfast.

Little Tommy Tucker,
Sings for his supper:
What shall we give him?
White bread and butter.
How shall he cut it
Without a knife?
How will he be married
Without a wife?

55

Jenny Wren fell sick
Upon a merry time,
In came Robin Redbreast
And brought her sops and wine.

Eat well of the sop, Jenny,
Drink well of the wine.
Thank you, Robin, kindly,
You shall be mine.

Jenny Wren got well,
And stood upon her feet;
And told Robin plainly,
She loved him not a bit.

Robin he got angry,
And hopped upon a twig,
Saying, Out upon you, fie upon you!
Bold faced jig!

56

Pat-a-cake, pat-a-cake, baker's man,
Bake me a cake as fast as you can;
Pat it and prick it, and mark it with B,
Put it in the oven for baby and me.

To market, to market, to buy a fat pig,
Home again, home again, jiggety-jig;
To market, to market, to buy a fat hog,
Home again, home again, jiggety-jog.

Tom, Tom, the piper's son,
Stole a pig and away he run;
The pig was eat
And Tom was beat,
And Tom went howling down the street.

The Hare and the Tortoise

A hare came leaping across the field. He loved darting this way and that, stopping to look and listen, then to be off again as fast as he could go.

He was at the hedge, nosing his way through into a grassy lane when he saw the tortoise. Hare sat up on his strong hind legs, ears held high and his whiskers twitching. He always laughed at Tortoise – that heavy shell, the funny wrinkled face and neck poking out in front, and those bent legs! . . . How could anyone walk on such legs?

"Poor old Tortoise," he chuckled. "He is so slow . . . Slow as a snail!"

Then he called:

"Hallo there, Tortoise! . . . Are you walking your slowest or your fastest?"

"Always at the same pace, Hare," the tortoise replied. "Just slow but sure."

"There's one thing for sure," teased the hare, "you'll always be the last getting there – wherever it might be!"

"Oh, I don't know," Tortoise answered in his calm, thoughtful way. "I think we should have a race. I will win of course."

This amused the hare so much he was quite doubled up with laughter.

"Do you . . . mean that?" he choked, trying to take a deep breath.

"Of course! I always mean what I say," said the tortoise.

A fox was peeping from behind a tree, listening and grinning with delight at what he heard.

'This will be fun,' he thought and came forward hoping to take part in some way.

"Good morning, gentlemen! . . . Can I help? . . . Get things going, perhaps?" he asked.

All the woodland animals stood by chatting and waiting to see the race.

When they'd agreed on how far to go and which tree should be the winning post, the hare and the tortoise stood ready at the starting line.

Fox gave the signal . . . They were off!

The hare bounded away and reached the top of the next hill in no time at all. There he stopped to look back.

"Poor old Tortoise," he said to himself, "not even in sight . . . Beat me indeed! . . . I might as well have a rest."

So, he settled down in the cool grass and fell fast asleep.

Meanwhile, the tortoise plodded on; step by step, never looking round, never stopping. He just kept doing what he'd made up his mind to do. Fox saw it all and smiled.

The other animals took a short cut across the field and were there at the post to watch for the winner.

It was a very hot day. The sun began to burn the hare's nose and so he woke up. The fox, waiting behind the hedge, turned and made a dash for the finishing line.

Hare sat up, rubbing his eyes, wondering what he was doing there.

"Oh yes, of course, the race," he mumbled. "Where's poor old Tortoise now?" and he glanced down the lane. There was no sign of those funny little legs. Hare looked the other way; the lane was empty.

"Ah well, I'd better push on. . . . I'll give him a wave as I pass," and Hare giggled to think of it.

There was the winning post, round the next bend, and every-body was jumping up and down with excitement.

'How nice!' Hare thought. 'My friends have come to cheer me.' Then he heard the words, "Come on, Tortoise . . . Only a few steps . . . That's it! . . . You've WON! . . . Good old Tortoise!"

Hare arrived feeling very foolish.

"How did you manage it, Tortoise?" everyone was asking.

"Well, slow and steady wins the race," he replied and started nibbling a juicy leaf.

I don't think Hare teased him any more – do you?

This is the house that Jack built.

This is the malt
That lay in the house that Jack built.

This is the rat,
That ate the malt
That lay in the house that Jack built.

This is the cat,
That killed the rat,
That ate the malt
That lay in the house that Jack built.

This is the dog,
That worried the cat,
That killed the rat,
That ate the malt
That lay in the house that Jack built.

This is the cow with the crumpled horn,
That tossed the dog,
That worried the cat,
That killed the rat,
That ate the malt
That lay in the house that Jack built.

This is the maiden all forlorn,
That milked the cow with the crumpled horn,
That tossed the dog,
That worried the cat,
That killed the rat,
That ate the malt
That lay in the house that Jack built.

This is the man all tattered and torn,
That kissed the maiden all forlorn,
That milked the cow with the crumpled horn,
That tossed the dog,
That worried the cat,
That killed the rat,
That ate the malt
That lay in the house that Jack built.

This is the priest all shaven and shorn,
That married the man all tattered and torn,
That kissed the maiden all forlorn,
That milked the cow with the crumpled horn,
That tossed the dog,
That worried the cat,
That killed the rat,
That ate the malt
That lay in the house that Jack built.

This is the cock that crowed in the morn,
That waked the priest all shaven and shorn,
That married the man all tattered and torn,
That kissed the maiden all forlorn,
That milked the cow with the crumpled horn,
That tossed the dog,
That worried the cat,
That killed the rat,
That ate the malt
That lay in the house that Jack built.

This is the farmer sowing his corn,
That kept the cock that crowed in the morn,
That waked the priest all shaven and shorn,
That married the man all tattered and torn,
That kissed the maiden all forlorn,
That milked the cow with the crumpled horn,
That tossed the dog,
That worried the cat,
That killed the rat,
That ate the malt
That lay in the house that Jack built.

Once I saw a little bird
Come hop, hop, hop,
And I cried, Little bird,
Will you stop, stop, stop?

I was going to the window
To say, How do you do?
But he shook his little tail
And away he flew.

Chicken Licken

One morning, when Chicken Licken was sitting under an oak tree, an acorn fell upon his head.

"Oh dear," he gasped, "The sky is falling. I must run and tell the King."

On the way to the palace he met his friend Henny Penny.

"Where are you going?" asked Henny Penny.

"To tell the King the sky is falling," said Chicken Licken.

"Then I'll come with you," clucked Henny Penny.

Cocky Locky was scratching for grain.

"Where are you both going in such a hurry?" he asked.

"To tell the King the sky is falling," said Chicken Licken.

"Then I'll come with you," crowed Cocky Locky.

"Where are you all going?" asked Ducky Lucky, when she met them hurrying along a footpath.

"To tell the King the sky is falling," said Chicken Licken without stopping.

"Then I'll come with you," quacked Ducky Lucky.

"Where are you all going?" called Drakey Lakey from the pond.

"To tell the King the sky is falling," said Chicken Licken.

"Then I'll come with you," said Drakey Lakey shaking the water from his webbed feet.

Goosey Loosey was as anxious as everyone else to help tell the King the bad news.

"I'll come with you," she hissed as she stretched her long white neck.

"And I'll come too . . . too . . . too . . ." gobbled Turkey Lurkey who didn't like to be left out of anything.

Foxy Loxy was lurking behind a bush.

"Where are you all going in such a hurry?" he asked slyly.

"To tell the King the sky is falling," said Chicken Licken.

"Then you had better follow me," said Foxy Loxy. "I know of a short cut."

And he led Chicken Licken, Henny Penny, Cocky Locky, Ducky Lucky, Drakey Lakey, Goosey Loosey and Turkey Lurkey through the bushes to his den, where his wife and five hungry children were waiting.

And that, I am sorry to say, was the end of Chicken Licken, Henny Penny, Cocky Locky, Ducky Lucky, Drakey Lakey, Goosey Loosey and Turkey Lurkey, for the fox family had them for dinner, and the King never did find out that a piece of sky had fallen on Chicken Licken's head.

The Owl and the Pussy-cat went to sea
In a beautiful pea-green boat,
They took some honey, and plenty of money,
Wrapped up in a five-pound note.
The Owl looked up to the stars above,
And sang to a small guitar,
'O lovely Pussy! Pussy, my love,
What a beautiful Pussy you are,
    You are,
    You are!
What a beautiful Pussy you are!'

Pussy said to the Owl, 'You elegant fowl!
How charmingly sweet you sing!
O let us be married! too long we have tarried:
But what shall we do for a ring?'
They sailed away, for a year and a day,
To the land where the Bong-tree grows,
And there in a wood a Piggy-wig stood
With a ring at the end of his nose,
    His nose,
    His nose,
With a ring at the end of his nose.

'Dear Pig, are you willing to sell for one shilling
Your ring?' Said the Piggy, 'I will'.
So they took it away, and were married next day
By the Turkey who lives on the hill.
They dined on mince, and slices of quince,
Which they ate with a runcible spoon;
And hand in hand, on the edge of the sand,
They danced by the light of the moon,
    The moon,
    The moon,
They danced by the light of the moon.

*O*ranges and lemons,
Say the bells of St. Clement's.

You owe me five farthings,
Say the bells of St. Martin's.

When will you pay me?
Say the bells of Old Bailey.

When I grow rich,
Say the bells of Shoreditch.

When will that be?
Say the bells of Stepney.

I'm sure I don't know,
Says the great bell at Bow.

Here comes a candle to light you to bed,
Here comes a chopper to chop off your head.

The Magic Porridge Pot

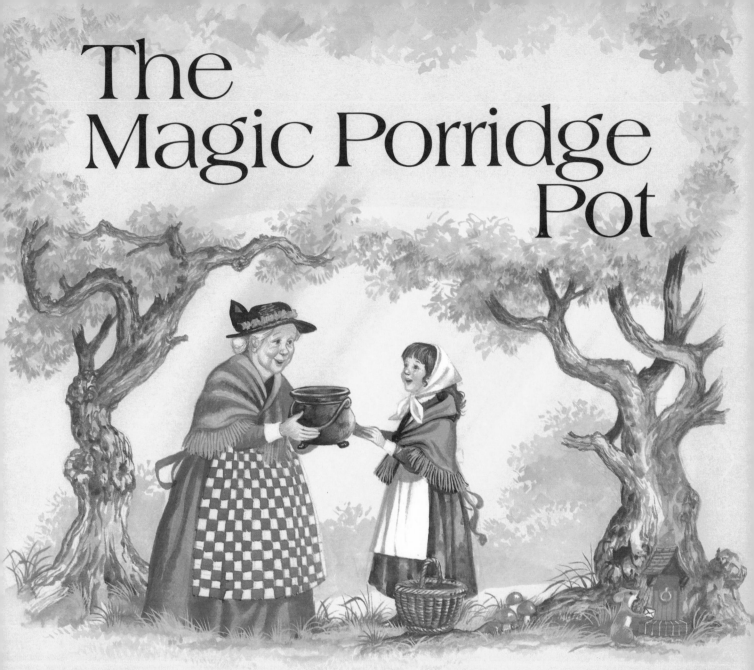

Once, there was a girl who lived with her mother in a tiny house on the outskirts of a small town. They were very poor and sometimes they were very hungry. Often they had nothing to eat at all.

One day, when the girl was out in the woods looking for mushrooms and blackberries, she met an old woman who was carrying an empty iron pot.

"Take it," said the old woman. She put the pot into the girl's hands. "Whenever you are hungry, say to it, 'Little pot boil.' When you have enough, say, 'Little pot, stop'."

The girl thought it very strange, but she took the pot home and told her mother what the old woman had said.

"Put the pot on the table, say the words and we shall see what happens," said her mother.

"Little pot, boil," said the girl. As soon as she spoke, the pot began to bubble and hiss and steam began to rise from it.

"It's filling up," gasped the girl.

"It is truly a magic pot," said her mother. "Stop it, before it overflows."

"Little pot, stop," said the girl. The bubbling and hissing stopped at once. "What a lovely smell," she said.

"That looks and smells like porridge to me," said her mother. "Bring two plates and two spoons and we will taste it."

It was the sweetest, creamiest, nicest porridge they had ever tasted. With a magic porridge pot like that, their days of being hungry were over. It did not matter how much porridge they ate, there was always more to be had when they said the magic words, 'Little pot, boil.'

One day, when the girl was out, her mother set the pot on the table and said,

"Little pot, boil."

The bubbling began, the steam began to rise and the lovely smell of porridge filled the room. The sweet creamy porridge reached the top of the pot. The girl's mother opened her mouth to say the words to stop the pot, but she could not remember them. All she could think of to say was "Um, er . . . that's enough." A tiny trickle of porridge began to run down the outside of the porridge pot. That had never happened before.

"Stop . . . stop . . ." she cried. "I don't want any more . . . Stop filling up . . . Oh, dear, oh dear . . ." She just could not remember the right words.

The pot bubbled and bubbled. The trickle of porridge became a stream. It spread across the table and fell in a sticky mess to the floor.

"Whatever shall I do?" she cried as she climbed onto a chair. "Please . . . please . . . please stop . . . please pot!"

The pool of porridge spread to the door and outside along the street.

"Stop! . . . Stop! . . ." she shouted. "Come back porridge, get back into the pot . . . please stop!" The porridge took no notice. It would only stop if the right words were spoken. What were the right words?

The sweet creamy porridge became like an overflowing river. It ran on and on, through the streets, into all the houses and the dog kennels. It filled up the fish ponds and the drains.

"What is happening?" cried the people in the town. They took off their shoes and waded through the sticky mess.

"It's the pot . . . it will not stop," cried the girl's mother.

The dogs began to bark, the cats began to howl and everyone began to shout at the porridge pot.

"Stop making porridge before we all drown . . . Stop! Stop! . . ."

The girl was at her uncle's house at the other side of the town. She heard the noise outside and looked out of the window to see what was happening. As soon as she saw the river of porridge oozing through the streets, she knew just what to do. She ran home as fast as she could, through the sticky porridge.

When she came to the house, her mother was still shouting at the pot. "Stop cooking . . . stop bubbling . . . Stop! . . . Stop! . . ."

"Little pot, stop," said the girl. Those were the magic words and the pot did stop instantly.

"I will only use the pot in future when you are here," said the girl's mother. "I don't want that to happen again."

It took many days to clean up the mess because the porridge had stuck to everything. Perhaps it was not a good thing after all, to have a magic porridge pot.

Solomon Grundy,
Born on a Monday,
Christened on Tuesday,
Married on Wednesday,
Took ill on Thursday,
Worse on Friday,
Died on Saturday,
Buried on Sunday.
This is the end
Of Solomon Grundy.

Mary had a little lamb,
It's fleece was white as snow;
And everywhere that Mary went
The lamb was sure to go.

It followed her to school one day,
That was against the rule;
It made the children laugh and play
To see a lamb at school.

And so the teacher turned it out,
But still it lingered near,
And waited patiently about
Till Mary did appear.

Why does the lamb love Mary so?
The eager children cry;
Why, Mary loves the lamb, you know,
The teacher did reply.

One, two, three, four,
Mary at the cottage door,
Five, six, seven, eight,
Eating cherries off a plate.

What are little boys made of?
What are little boys made of?
Frogs and snails
And puppy-dogs' tails,
That's what little boys are made of.

What are little girls made of?
What are little girls made of?
Sugar and spice
And all that's nice,
That's what little girls are made of.

London Bridge is broken down,
Broken down, broken down,
London Bridge is broken down,
My fair lady.

Build it up with wood and clay,
Wood and clay, wood and clay,
Build it up with wood and clay,
My fair lady.

Wood and clay will wash away,
Wash away, wash away,
Wood and clay will wash away,
My fair lady.

Build it up with bricks and mortar,
Bricks and mortar, bricks and mortar,
Build it up with bricks and mortar,
My fair lady.

Bricks and mortar will not stay,
Will not stay, will not stay,
Bricks and mortar will not stay,
My fair lady.

Build it up with iron and steel,
Iron and steel, iron and steel,
Build it up with iron and steel,
My fair lady.

Iron and steel will bend and bow,
Bend and bow, bend and bow,
Iron and steel will bend and bow,
My fair lady.

Build it up with silver and gold,
Silver and gold, silver and gold,
Build it up with silver and gold,
My fair lady.

Silver and gold will be stolen away,
Stolen away, stolen away,
Silver and gold will be stolen away,
My fair lady.

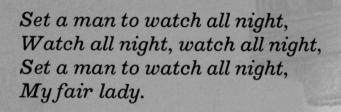

Set a man to watch all night,
Watch all night, watch all night,
Set a man to watch all night,
My fair lady.

Suppose the man should fall asleep,
Fall asleep, fall asleep,
Suppose the man should fall asleep?
My fair lady.

Give him a pipe to smoke all night,
Smoke all night, smoke all night,
Give him a pipe to smoke all night,
My fair lady.

Little Bob Robin,
Where do you live?
Up in yonder wood, sir,
On a hazel twig.

Little Betty Blue
Lost her holiday shoe,
What can little Betty do?
Give her another
To match the other,
And then she may walk out in two.

Cinderella

There was once a girl called Cinderella. She lived with her father and her step-sisters in a huge house. Cinderella was beautiful. Her step-sisters were ugly. Cinderella was kind and gentle. Her step-sisters were unkind and spiteful. They spent their time trying to make themselves look pretty and they made sure Cinderella spent her time cleaning and washing and scrubbing so that no one would notice she was more beautiful than they.

One morning, when Cinderella was scrubbing floors, there was a great commotion.

"Look what we've got," cried the ugly sisters, dancing round and round the kitchen and leaving a pattern of big muddy footmarks all over the newly washed floor. They dangled a gilt-edged card under Cinderella's nose. "We have got an invitation to the King's ball. We are going to meet the Prince. I dare say he will want to marry one of us."

"Oh please . . . may I go to the ball?" asked Cinderella. The ugly sisters hooted with laughter.

"You . . . go to the ball . . . how silly you are. You haven't a thing to wear." Which was perfectly true. Poor Cinderella only had a brown ragged dress and a sackcloth apron. "And besides, we will need *you* to help *us* get ready."

The ugly sisters had a wardrobe full of beautiful ball gowns and trunks full of elaborate wigs. They had boxes, and boxes, of sweet smelling powder. They had countless bottles of sweet smelling lotions. It took them hours and hours to get ready to go anywhere, let alone somewhere as important as the King's ball.

On the night of the ball they led poor Cinderella a merry dance.

"Fetch that . . . alter this . . . press that . . . tie this . . . find that . . . do it this way . . . undo it . . . do it up . . . stop pulling . . . pull it tighter . . ." Poor Cinderella felt quite dizzy by the time they were both powdered and bewigged and fastened into their ball gowns.

"Wash the dishes . . . make up the fire . . . have supper waiting." they called as they swept grandly to their waiting carriage looking not the tiniest bit beautiful.

Poor Cinderella. She did the chores then sat beside the fire and wept. She did so want to go to the ball.

Suddenly there was a flash of light. She thought at first it was a burst of sparks from the fire and then she saw a strange little woman wearing a pointed hat and carrying a wand of dancing stars.

"Do not be afraid," she said, "I am your fairy Godmother. You shall go to the ball."

"But I have no dress to wear," said Cinderella sadly. "I cannot go to the ball wearing rags."

"You are not wearing rags now," said the fairy. She had touched Cinderella's tattered brown dress with her wand. She had changed it into a beautiful ball gown and had put glass slippers on Cinderella's bare feet.

The fairy called for a pumpkin. She touched that with her wand and turned it into a coach. She turned eight white mice into eight white horses. Six green lizards into six liveried footmen.

A rat into a coachman.

"You must be home by midnight," said the fairy as Cinderella stepped into the coach. "My magic stops at midnight and your ball gown will become rags again."

Cinderella danced with the King's son all evening. He couldn't take his eyes off her. He thought her the most beautiful girl he had ever seen. Cinderella had never been so happy in her life. She was so happy she forgot time was ticking past and it wasn't until the clock began to strike twelve that she remembered the fairy's warning.

"Wait . . ." cried the Prince, as she slipped from his arms, "You haven't told me your name . . ."

There was no time to stop. Cinderella ran from the ballroom without a backward glance.
Seven . . . eight . . . nine . . . she lost a slipper as she ran down the palace steps. She did not dare stop to pick it up . . .
Ten . . . eleven . . . on the twelfth stroke her beautiful ball gown became rags and her coach turned back into a pumpkin. She ran home with her feet bare and with the mice, the rat and the lizards scurrying behind her.

But one thing hadn't changed and that was the glass slipper which lay on the palace steps. It was the Prince himself who found it. He recognised it at once.

"I will marry the girl who can wear this slipper," he said, "No matter who she is."

He sent messengers across the land with orders that every girl in the kingdom was to try the slipper. Eventually they came to the house where Cinderella and her step-sisters lived. The ugly sisters were so excited. They snatched the glass slipper from the messenger before he could say a word.

"Look . . . it fits me . . ." said the eldest.

"But your heel is hanging out," said the messenger.

"It fits me . . . it fits me . . ." said the youngest.

"But your toes are bent double," said the messenger, and then he asked, "Is there anyone else who would like to try the slipper?"

Before Cinderella could answer one of the ugly sisters clapped a hand over her mouth.

"She's only a serving maid . . . the slipper won't fit her."

But the messenger had his orders. Of course, the slipper fitted Cinderella perfectly. As she slipped her foot into it her fairy godmother appeared with her magic wand in one hand and the second glass slipper in the other.

"Cinderella shall marry the Prince," she said, and with a touch of her wand she changed Cinderella's rags into the beautiful gown she had worn at the ball.

"It was you . . . it was you who stole the Prince from us . . ."
shouted the ugly sisters, their eyes nearly popping out of their
heads. "It's not fair . . . it's not fair . . ." They stamped their feet
and pouted and sulked. No one took any notice of them at all. There
was a royal wedding to plan and that was far more important.

Ride a cock-horse to Banbury Cross,
To buy little Johnny a galloping horse;
It trots behind and it ambles before,
And Johnny shall ride till he can ride no more.

hree blind mice, see how they run!
They all ran after the farmer's wife,
Who cut off their tails with a carving knife,
Did you ever see such a thing in your life,
As three blind mice?

95

Little Robin Redbreast sat upon a tree,
Up went pussy cat, and down went she;
Down came pussy, and away Robin ran;
Says little Robin Redbreast, Catch me if you can.
Little Robin Redbreast jumped upon a wall,
Pussy cat jumped after him, and almost got a fall;
Little Robin chirped and sang, and what did pussy say?
Pussy cat said, Mew, and Robin jumped away.

How many miles to Babylon?
Three score miles and ten.
Can I get there by candle-light?
Yes, and back again.
If your heels are nimble and light,
You may get there by candle-light.

Hush-a-bye, baby, on the tree top,
When the wind blows the cradle will rock;
When the bough breaks the cradle will fall,
Down will come baby, cradle, and all.

ld King Cole
Was a merry old soul,
And a merry old soul was he;
He called for his pipe,
And he called for his bowl,
And he called for his fiddlers three.

Every fiddler, he had a fiddle,
And a very fine fiddle had he;
Twee tweedle dee, tweedle dee, went the fiddlers.
Oh, there's none so rare
As can compare
With King Cole and his fiddlers three.

Foolish Jack

Foolish Jack never stopped to think things out for himself. And sometimes, as you can well imagine, that led him into trouble.

One day his mother sent him out to work. He raked hay all day for the farmer and at the end of the day the farmer gave him a penny. Jack tied the penny in his handkerchief, but somewhere on the way home, he lost the handkerchief and the penny.

"You silly boy!" said his mother. "You should have put it in your pocket."

Next day Jack went to work at the dairy. When evening came the dairyman gave him a jug of milk.

Jack did not want to lose the milk as he had lost the penny, so he put the jug in his pocket. He had to tip it on its side to get it in, and of course it spilt. What a mess it made.

"You silly boy!" said his mother, when he got home. "You should have carried it on your head."

The following day Jack helped the man who kept hens. He gave Jack six brown eggs to take home.

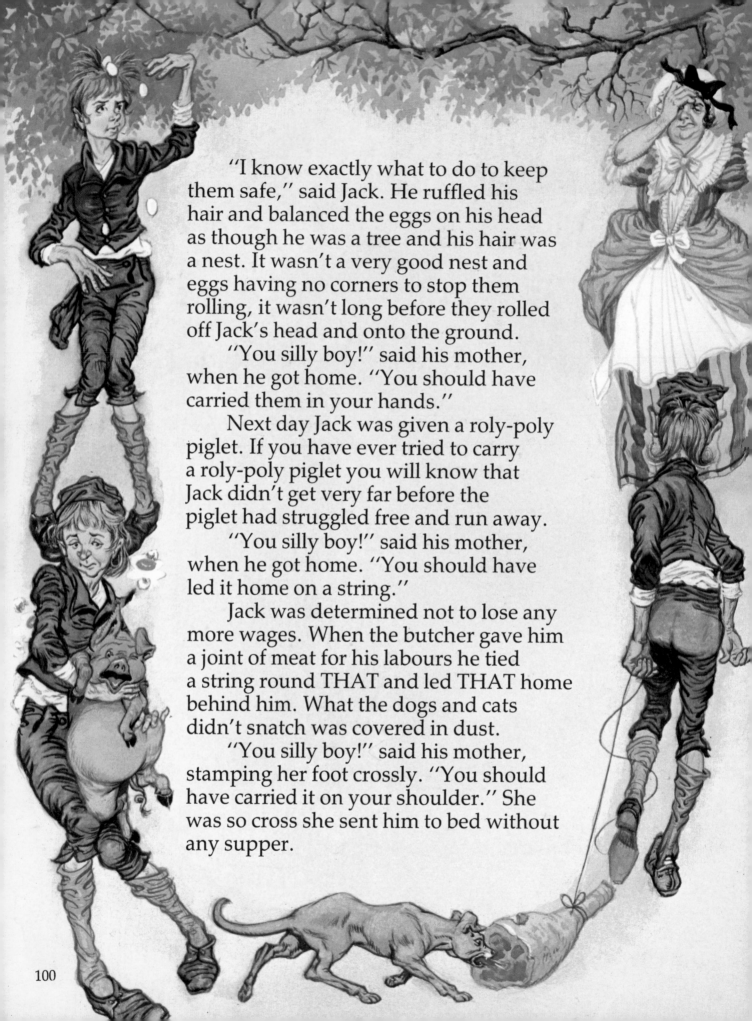

"I know exactly what to do to keep them safe," said Jack. He ruffled his hair and balanced the eggs on his head as though he was a tree and his hair was a nest. It wasn't a very good nest and eggs having no corners to stop them rolling, it wasn't long before they rolled off Jack's head and onto the ground.

"You silly boy!" said his mother, when he got home. "You should have carried them in your hands."

Next day Jack was given a roly-poly piglet. If you have ever tried to carry a roly-poly piglet you will know that Jack didn't get very far before the piglet had struggled free and run away.

"You silly boy!" said his mother, when he got home. "You should have led it home on a string."

Jack was determined not to lose any more wages. When the butcher gave him a joint of meat for his labours he tied a string round THAT and led THAT home behind him. What the dogs and cats didn't snatch was covered in dust.

"You silly boy!" said his mother, stamping her foot crossly. "You should have carried it on your shoulder." She was so cross she sent him to bed without any supper.

And then Jack's luck changed, though
it didn't seem like it to begin with.
He had worked all day for the goatherd
and had been given a goat to take home.

Now it so happened that on the way
home every day Jack had to pass the house
of a rich man. The rich man had a
beautiful daughter who had never laughed,
and he promised that the first person
to make her laugh should marry her.

She had watched Jack go by the house
every day. When she saw him trying to
carry eggs on his head, her eyes had
twinkled. When she saw him trying to
carry a roly-poly piglet she had smiled,
just a little. On the day he came past
the house with a protesting goat wrapped
round his neck like a scarf and with his
own knees buckling beneath him, she burst
into merry peals of laughter.

And that was how Jack found a wife.
She was as sensible as she was rich, and
she taught Jack how to think for himself,
and so they lived happily ever after.

Old Mother Hubbard
Went to the cupboard,
To fetch her poor dog a bone;
But when she came there
The cupboard was bare
And so the poor dog had none.

She went to the baker's
To buy him some bread;
But when she came back
The poor dog was dead.

She went to the undertaker's
To buy him a coffin;
But when she came back
The poor dog was laughing.

She took a clean dish
To get him some tripe;
But when she came back
He was smoking a pipe.

She went to the alehouse
To get him some beer;
But when she came back
The dog sat in a chair.

She went to the tavern
For white wine and red;
But when she came back
The dog stood on his head.

She went to the fruiterer's
To buy him some fruit;
But when she came back
He was playing the flute.

She went to the tailor's
To buy him a coat;
But when she came back
He was riding a goat.

She went to the hatter's
To buy him a hat;
But when she came back
He was feeding the cat.

She went to the barber's
To buy him a wig;
But when she came back
He was dancing a jig.

She went to the cobbler's
To buy him some shoes;
But when she came back
He was reading the news.

She went to the seamstress
To buy him some linen;
But when she came back
The dog was a-spinning.

She went to the hosier's
To buy him some hose;
But when she came back
He was dressed in his clothes.

The dame made a curtsy,
The dog made a bow;
The dame said, Your servant,
The dog said, Bow-wow.

Puss in Boots

Once upon a time, there was a miller, who had three sons. When he died he left his mill to his first son, his donkey to his second son, and because he had nothing else, he left his cat to his third son.

The first son ground flour at the mill and sold it. The second son harnessed the donkey to a cart and carried things for paying customers. But what could the third son do with a cat, except let him sit in the sun, and purr, and drink milk?

One day, the cat said, "Master, give me a pair of boots and a sack and you will see that I am not as useless as you think." It was a very strange request for a cat to make, but it was granted nonetheless.

The cat, or Puss in Boots, as the miller's son now called him, went into the forest and caught a rabbit. He put it in the sack and then instead of taking it home to the miller's son, he took it to the King's palace.

"Please accept this small present from my master the Marquis of Carabas," said Puss in Boots.

It was to be the first of many presents Puss in Boots took to the King, and each time he said he had been sent by his master the Marquis of Carabas. And though the King never actually met the Marquis of Carabas, he soon became very familiar with his name. The miller's son knew nothing of the presents, or of the Marquis of Carabas, and Puss in Boots didn't tell him.

One day, when Puss in Boots was at the palace, he overheard someone say that the King was about to take his daughter for a drive in the country. Puss in Boots hurried home.

"Quick master!" he called. "Go and bathe in the river and I will make your fortune."

It was another strange request for a cat to make but the miller's son was used to his pet by now and so he did as he was told. No sooner was he in the river than Puss in Boots took his clothes and threw them into the river with him.

"Puss . . . Puss . . . what are you doing?" called the miller's son.

Puss didn't answer, he was watching the road. Presently he saw the King's carriage in the distance. He waited until it was close then he ran out in the road in front of it.

"Help! Help! My master the Marquis of Carabas is drowning! Please save him!"

It took but a moment to drag the miller's son, who hadn't the slightest idea what Puss in Boots was up to, from the river and find him some dry clothes. He looked so handsome in the fine velvet tunic and the doublet and hose borrowed from one of the footmen that the princess fell in love with him at once.

"Father dear, may the Marquis of Carabas ride with us?"

The King liked to please his daughter and agreed to her request at once.

"Will you ride with us Puss?" asked the King.

Puss asked to be excused. He said he had something rather important to attend to. He ran on ahead of the carriage, and each time he saw someone at work in the fields he called,

"If the King asks who this land belongs to, tell him it belongs to the Marquis of Carabas."

The King did stop the carriage several times, and each time he received the same answer to his question.

'The Marquis of Carabas must be a very rich man,' he thought.

Puss in Boots ran so swiftly that soon he was a long way ahead of the carriage. Presently he came to a rich and imposing looking castle, which he knew belonged to a cruel and wicked ogre. He went straight up to the ogre without so much as a twitching of a whisker, and said,

"I hear you can turn yourself into any animal you choose. I won't believe a story like that unless I see it for myself."

Immediately, the ogre changed himself into a lion, and roared and growled and snarled.

"There . . ." he said, when he had turned himself back into an ogre. "I hope I frightened you."

"Must be easy to change yourself into something big," said Puss in Boots with a shrug. "I don't suppose you can turn yourself into something as small as a . . . er . . . um . . ." He seemed to be thinking. ". . . er . . . um . . . a mouse?"

The ogre couldn't have a mere cat doubting his special abilities. He changed himself into a tiny mouse in the twinkling of an eye. It was the last time he changed himself into anything because Puss in Boots pounced on him and ate him up before he could change back into an ogre, and THAT was the end of him!

"Hoorah!" shouted the castle servants. "We are free of the wicked ogre at last. Hoorah!"

"Your new master will always be kind, you can be sure of that," said Puss in Boots.

"Who IS our new master?" they asked.

"The Marquis of Carabas of course," said Puss.

When the King's carriage reached the castle, Puss in Boots was standing at the drawbridge, with the smiling servants gathered round him.

"Welcome. ." he said with a beautiful bow. "Welcome to the home of my master the Marquis of Carabas." The miller's son was too astonished to do anything except think to himself,

'Whatever is Puss up to?'

Luckily Puss had time to explain while the King was getting out of the carriage.

'What a rich man this Marquis must be,' thought the King. 'And such a nice young man too.'

Not long afterwards the princess and the miller's son were married. They, and Puss in Boots, lived happily ever after in the castle that had once belonged to the wicked ogre.

Simple Simon met a pieman,
Going to the fair;
Says Simple Simon to the pieman,
Let me taste your ware.

Says the pieman to Simple Simon,
Show me first your penny;
Says Simple Simon to the pieman
Indeed I have not any.

Simple Simon went a-fishing,
For to catch a whale;
All the water he had got
Was in his mother's pail.

Simple Simon went to look
If plums grew on a thistle;
He pricked his fingers very much,
Which made poor Simon whistle.

He went for water in a sieve
But soon it all fell through;
And now poor Simple Simon
Bids you all adieu.

Rock-a-bye baby,
Thy cradle is green,
Father's a nobleman,
Mother's a queen;
And Betty's a lady,
And wears a gold ring;
And Johnny's a drummer,
And drums for the king.

Humpty Dumpty sat on a wall,
Humpty Dumpty had a great fall.
All the king's horses,
And all the king's men,
Couldn't put Humpty together again.

Hark, hark,
The dogs do bark,
The beggars are coming to town;
Some in rags,
And some in jags,
And one in a velvet gown.

Come, let's to bed,
Says Sleepy-head;
Tarry a while, says Slow;
Put on the pot,
Says Greedy-gut,
We'll sup before we go.

114

Cock Robin got up early
At the break of day,
And went to Jenny's window
To sing a roundelay.
He sang Cock Robin's love
To little Jenny Wren,
And when he got unto the end
Then he began again.

115

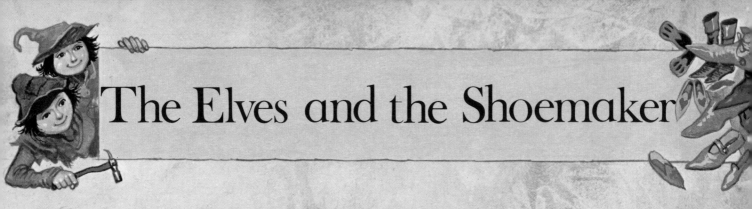

The Elves and the Shoemaker

Once there was a shoemaker. He worked hard, but times were hard and the day came when he was left with just enough leather to make one pair of shoes. He cut the pieces very carefully. One mistake, and there wouldn't have been enough leather to make even one pair. He put the pieces on the bench so that he could begin stitching them together the next morning and went to bed.

During the night, as he and his wife slept, something very mysterious happened.

"Wife! Come quickly!" he called when he went to start work next day.

On the bench, where the pieces of shoe leather had been, was now as fine a pair of finished shoes as they had ever seen.

"How could that have happened?" gasped his wife.

"We must have a friend," said the shoemaker. "And look how well they are made. I couldn't have made them better myself."

He sold the shoes that very morning, and for a very good price. Now he could buy enough leather to make two pairs of shoes. He cut the pieces and left them on his bench as he had done the previous night. When he came down to breakfast the following morning there were four finished shoes on the bench. And so it continued, night after night, after night. The more leather he was able to buy the more shoes he was able to cut. The more pieces he left on his bench, the more finished shoes he found in the morning. The more finished shoes he found, the more leather he was able to buy. It wasn't long before he began to grow rich for the shoes were so beautifully made everyone wanted to own a pair.

One evening, not long before Christmas, his wife said,
"I wish we knew who was making the shoes so that
we could thank them." The shoemaker wished the
same thing himself, and they decided, there and
then, that instead of going to bed that night they
would stay up and keep watch.

At midnight the door opened and two elves
came into the shop. They sat cross-legged
on the bench and worked hard and
diligently till all the pieces of leather
had been sewn into shoes,
and then they left, as quietly
as they had arrived.

The shoemaker and his
wife crept from their
hiding place.

17

Naturally, they were astonished by what they had seen, but try as they would, they could think of no way of thanking the fairy-cobblers until the wife said,

"Did you notice how ragged their clothes were? I will make them each a new suit."

The shoemaker jumped to his feet and said,

"Did you notice that their feet were bare? I will make them both a pair of shoes."

The shoemaker and his wife were so pleased with their idea that they set to work the very next day. By Christmas Eve they had finished. The shoemaker had made four tiny shoes from the softest leather he could buy. His wife had made two pairs of tiny green breeches, two elegant green coats and two tiny frilled shirts, two pairs of white ribbed stockings which she had knitted on darning needles and two jaunty caps each trimmed with a mottled feather. They had taken as much care with their work as the elves had with theirs.

That night, instead of laying the pieces of shoe leather on the work bench they set out the new clothes. And then they hid and kept watch. At the stroke of midnight the two elves crept into the shop. When they saw the two sets of clothes they shouted with delight and threw down their shoemaking tools.

"We need make shoes no more," they sang, as they pulled on their white stockings. They danced from the shop dressed from tip to toe in their new clothes, as happy as any two elves could possibly be.

"How pleased they were," said the shoemaker as he hugged his wife.

"How elegant they looked," said the wife as she hugged the shoemaker.

The shoemaker and his wife never saw the elves again. But their luck had changed and the shoes the shoemaker made sold just as well as the shoes the elves made, and he and his wife prospered and were happy ever after.

The lion and the unicorn
Were fighting for the crown;
The lion beat the unicorn
All round about the town.

Some gave them white bread,
And some gave them brown;
Some gave them plum cake
And drummed them out of town.

Little Boy Blue,
Come blow your horn,
The sheep's in the meadow,
The cow's in the corn;
But where is the boy
Who looks after the sheep?
He's under a haystack,
Fast asleep.
Will you wake him?
No, not I,
For if I do,
He's sure to cry.

Yankee Doodle came to town,
Riding on a pony;
He stuck a feather in his cap
And called it macaroni.

*ack and Jill went up the hill
To fetch a pail of water;
Jack fell down and broke his crown,
And Jill came tumbling after.*

*Up Jack got, and home did trot,
As fast as he could caper,
To old Dame Dob, who patched his nob
With vinegar and brown paper.*

The Enormous Turnip

Old Mr Poppascoff walked around his garden looking at his flowers and vegetables growing there. Then he saw the turnip!

"Come here, quickly," he called to his wife. "I only planted this yesterday. You can almost see it growing as you watch it."

"I don't like it," she whispered. "It's not right . . . it seems very strange to me."

Mr Poppascoff patted the turnip. "Now don't grow any more today . . . I'll come and see you in the morning."

Early the next morning, they woke to find the sun streaming in through the bedroom window. It was a lovely pale green. Mr Poppascoff padded over to the window in his bare feet.

"Oh dear!" he muttered. "Oh, my goodness me!" His wife came to see what he was looking at. She had to stand on tiptoe, as the floor was very cold.

"That wretched turnip!" she cried. "I knew there was something wrong as soon as I saw it."

They went down into the garden to have a look at it. The turnip was enormous. They fell over backwards, just trying to see the top and there they sat, staring up at it.

"Whatever shall we do?" wailed Mrs Poppascoff.

"Eat it, I hope," said her husband. He went to fetch a ladder and a saw to cut it down.

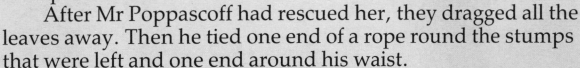

Up and up he climbed, while his wife held the ladder. Then, standing on the turnip top, he worked around, sawing the stalks off. Mrs Poppascoff sank beneath the falling leaves and was quite buried. She was not at all pleased.

After Mr Poppascoff had rescued her, they dragged all the leaves away. Then he tied one end of a rope round the stumps that were left and one end around his waist.

"Now, my dear," he said, "you push the turnip from that side. I will pull from this . . . we'll soon have it over."

But the turnip just wouldn't move.

"We'll both pull," said his wife.

So they pulled. Still the turnip wouldn't move.

Children coming home from school stopped to watch.

"Hi! . . . Johnny!" called Mr Poppascoff. "Come and help us pull up this turnip."

"Right," cried Johnny and he grabbed the old woman round her waist. They all pulled.

But still the turnip wouldn't move.

Johnny called to Sally, his sister, so she came to help.
"Pull!" cried Mr Poppascoff . . . "and again!"

They dug in their heels, they got red in the face, but try as hard as they could, nothing would move the turnip.

"Call the dog," Johnny said. So Mr Poppascoff whistled for Bess, the dog. She too, helped to pull. Still the turnip would not move.

Then, Tabitha the cat, came and held on to the dog's tail.

"This time we'll do it," cried the old man. . . . "Ready, steady, Pull! Pull as hard as you can!"

But still the turnip would not move.

Suddenly, a little mouse raced across the garden. Down went Tabitha's paw, right across the mouse's tail.

"You live here doing nothing for your keep," said the cat. "Now get under that turnip and nibble through it, before I nibble you! . . . Then come and help to pull."

So the little mouse did just as he was told. Then he twisted his tail round the cat's tail and he started to pull.

Once! Twice! . . . they pulled. Dirt and grit fell down on them like a shower of hailstones. Then all at once, the turnip shot out from the ground.

Everyone fell over in a heap! The little mouse pulled his tail away from the cat and ran. He didn't want to be squashed or nibbled.

Mr Poppascoff invited them all to supper.

"Bring your friends," he cried. "Bring everyone . . . You'll love my wife's turnip soup."

What a party! Everyone came and all the visitors had plenty to eat.

When they had gone, Bess and Tabitha lay snoozing on the mat, the little mouse was curled up in his hole and Mr Poppascoff and his wife sat watching the fire.

"It was a good party," said the old man.

"Very good," his wife agreed.

"No one could do better than that," he said. "Or grow such a turnip," he added. "I've never seen one like it before and there's plenty left."

"I don't want to see another turnip as long as I live!" cried the old woman. "I'm sick of turnips."

Silence . . . even the clock had stopped ticking. Slowly the old man turned to look at her.

"My dear, you can't mean that . . . whatever is wrong with seeing turnips? They are quite beautiful . . . but as long as I live I'll never EAT ANOTHER."

Mr Poppascoff and his wife fell back in their chairs. They laughed till the tears ran down their cheeks. The animals grinned, the clock ticked again and the fire sparkled once more in the grate.

If I had a donkey that wouldn't go,
Would I beat him? Oh no, no.
I'd put him in the barn and give him some corn,
The best little donkey that ever was born.

The north wind doth blow,
And we shall have snow,
And what will poor robin do then?
Poor thing.
He'll sit in a barn,
And keep himself warm,
And hide his head under his wing.
Poor thing.

Six little mice sat down to spin;
Pussy passed by and she peeped in.
What are you doing, my little men?
Weaving coats for gentlemen.
Shall I come in and cut off your threads?
No, no, Mistress Pussy, you'd bite off our heads.
Oh no, I'll not; I'll help you to spin.
That may be so, but you don't come in.

129

Tom, he was a piper's son,
He learnt to play when he was young,
And all the tune that he could play
Was, 'Over the hills and far away';
Over the hills and a great way off,
The wind shall blow my top-knot off.

Tom with his pipe made such a noise,
That he pleased both the girls and boys,
And they all stopped to hear him play,
'Over the hills and far away'.

Tom with his pipe did play with such skill
That those who heard him could never keep still;
As soon as he played they began for to dance,
Even pigs on their hind legs would after him prance.

As Dolly was milking her cow one day,
Tom took his pipe and began to play;
So Doll and the cow danced 'The Cheshire Round',
Till the pail was broken and the milk
ran on the ground.

He met old Dame Trot with a basket of eggs,
He used his pipe and she used her legs;
She danced about till the eggs were all broke,
She began for to fret, but he laughed at the joke.

Tom saw a cross fellow was beating an ass,
Heavy laden with pots, pans, dishes, and glass;
He took out his pipe and he played them a tune,
And the poor donkey's load was
lightened full soon.

Lavender's blue, diddle, diddle,
Lavender's green;
When I am king, diddle, diddle,
You shall be queen.

Call up your men, diddle, diddle,
Set them to work,
Some to the plough, diddle, diddle,
Some to the cart.

Some to make hay, diddle, diddle,
Some to thresh corn,
Whilst you and I, diddle, diddle,
Keep ourselves warm.

The Ugly Duckling

Once, somewhere in the country, there was a duck who had a clutch of eggs to hatch. Five of them hatched into fluffy little ducklings, but the sixth, which for some reason was bigger than all the others, lay in the nest, smooth and unbroken.

"Thats much too big to be a duck egg," said one of the duck's friends. "Looks more like a turkey egg to me."

"How will I be able to tell?" asked the duck.

"It will not swim when it is hatched," said her friend. "Turkeys never do."

But the egg wasn't a turkey egg because the bird that hatched from it DID swim. It swam as well as any duckling.

"That last duckling of yours is very ugly," laughed the farmyard hens. It was true. He wasn't a bit like his brothers and sisters.

"What an ugly duckling," laughed the geese when they saw him. And somehow that name stuck. Whenever anyone wanted him they called, "Ugly duckling, where are you?" or if they didn't want him they said "Ugly duckling go away." He even thought of himself as ugly duckling. He was very sad. He didn't like being ugly. He didn't like being teased. No one would play with him. No one would swim with him. Even his mother made fun of him. One day, the ugly duckling ran away. And I am sorry to say, no one missed him at all.

The ugly duckling hoped he would find someone in the big wide world, to be his friend. Someone who wouldn't mind how ugly he was. But the wild ducks were just as unkind as the farmyard ducks, and the wild geese honked at him and made fun, just as the farmyard geese had done.

"Am I never to find a friend? Am I never to be happy?" sighed the ugly duckling.

One day, as he sat alone and unhappy in the middle of a lake on the bleak flat marshes, he heard the steady beat of wings. When he looked up there were swans flying overhead with their long necks stretched before them and their white feathers gleaming in the sun. They were so beautiful. If only he had been born a swan. But he hadn't. He had been born a duckling and an ugly one at that.

The ugly duckling stayed on the lake
all through the long hard winter. Food
was hard to find and he was often hungry.
Once he was trapped in some ice and
thought he would die. He was set free,
just in time, by a farmer and his dog.

Spring came and the lake where he had
spent the lonely winter became a busy,
exciting, and noisy place. The ducks
were forever quacking and the geese were
forever honking. There was plenty of
splashing and excitement. But not for
the ugly duckling. No one quacked the
latest piece of gossip to him. Sadly he
spread his wings and took to the sky.
He had never flown before and he was
surprised how strong his wings were.
They carried him away from the lake and
the marshes and over a leafy garden.

On a still, clear pond in the garden,
he could see the beautiful white swans,
with their gracefully arched necks, and
suddenly the ugly duckling felt that he
did not want to live any longer.

"I will go down to the pond and ask
those beautiful birds to kill me," he
said. And down he went to the water.
He bent his head humbly and closed his
eyes.

"Kill me," he said to the swans. "I am too ugly to live."

"Ugly?" said the swans. "Have you looked at your reflection?"

"I do not need to look. I know how ugly I am," said the ugly duckling.

"Look into the water." said the swans. And so the ugly duckling did. What he saw made his heart beat fast and filled him with happiness. During the long winter months he had changed.

"I'm . . . I'm just like you . . ." he whispered.

When the children who lived in the garden came to feed the swans they called to one another,

"A new swan . . . a new swan . . . isn't he beautiful?" And then the ugly duckling knew without a doubt that he really WAS a swan, that he had ALWAYS been a swan and that his days of being lonely were over.

Who killed Cock Robin?
I, said the Sparrow,
With my bow and arrow,
I killed Cock Robin.

Who saw him die?
I, said the Fly,
With my little eye,
I saw him die.

Who caught his blood?
I, said the Fish,
With my little dish,
I caught his blood.

Who'll make the shroud?
I, said the Beetle,
With my thread and needle,
I'll make the shroud.

Who'll dig his grave?
I, said the Owl,
With my pick and shovel,
I'll dig his grave.

Who'll be the parson?
I, said the Rook,
With my little book,
I'll be the parson.

Who'll be the clerk?
I, said the Lark,
If it's not in the dark,
I'll be the clerk.

Who'll carry the link?
I, said the Linnet,
I'll fetch it in a minute,
I'll carry the link.

Who'll be chief mourner?
I, said the Dove,
I mourn for my love,
I'll be chief mourner.

Who'll carry the coffin?
I, said the Kite,
If it's not through the night,
I'll carry the coffin.

Who'll bear the pall?
We, said the Wren,
Both the cock and the hen,
We'll bear the pall.

Who'll sing a psalm?
I, said the Thrush,
As she sat on a bush,
I'll sing a psalm.

Who'll toll the bell?
I, said the Bull,
Because I can pull,
I'll toll the bell.

All the birds of the air
Fell a-sighing and a-sobbing,
When they heard the bell toll
For poor Cock Robin.

One, two, three, four, five,
Once I caught a fish alive,
Six, seven, eight, nine, ten,
Then I let it go again.

Why did you let it go?
Because it bit my finger so.
Which finger did it bite?
This little finger on the right.

I love little pussy,
Her coat is so warm,
And if I don't hurt her
She'll do me no harm.
So I'll not pull her tail,
Nor drive her away,
But pussy and I
Very gently will play.

Little Red Hen

Little Red Hen strutted out of the farmyard and into Farmer Brown's big field. The wheat had been cut and gathered so she could scratch about anywhere.

"I might find some ears of wheat that the farmer's men have dropped," she clucked.

And she did. They were fine fat ones, full of golden grains. She carried them back to the farmyard to show her friends.

"Cluck, cluck!" called Little Red Hen. "Will you help me plant these grains?"

"Oh, No-o-!" yawned Ginger Cat. "I'm too sleee-py." Ginger Cat went up onto the roof of the barn and went to sleep.

"Oh, No-o-!" squeaked Grey Rat. "I am busy storing winter food in the barn." Grey Rat scampered away.

"Oh, No-o!" grunted Pink Pig. "I am off to find some acorns." She trotted away into the trees.

"Very well," said Little Red Hen. "I will plant them myself."

And she did. She put them in fine straight rows. She watched the rows every day. She saw green shoots peeping up out of the ground. Then she saw the wheat at the top begin to ripen in the sunshine. Little Red Hen was pleased.

"My wheat is ready!" called Little
Red Hen to the animals. "Will you help
me gather it?"

"Not today," said Ginger Cat. "I
must wash my fur."

"Don't count on me," squeaked Grey
Rat. "My work is never done."

"You can see I'm too busy," grunted
Pink Pig. "I have ten piglets to feed!"

"Very well," said Little Red Hen.
"I will gather it myself."

And she did. She snipped each stalk
and made a neat bundle.

"That's done!" she clucked. "Will
you help me carry the wheat to the miller?
The miller will grind it into flour."

"Impossible!" said Ginger Cat opening
one eye.

"Quite impossible!" squeaked Grey Rat.

"Quite, quite impossible!" grunted
Pink Pig.

"Very well," said Little Red Hen,
"I will carry it myself."

And she did. She carried it all the
way to the mill. The great stones at the
mill turned round and round, grinding the
grains into flour. When the flour was
fine enough, the miller put it into a
linen bag.

"Thank you," said Little Red Hen.

When she came back to the farmyard, Little Red Hen called out,

"Here is the flour . . . Who will help me take it to the baker to be made into bread?"

"Out of the question," said Ginger Cat, walking away.

"Quite out of the question," squeaked Grey Rat, running off.

"Quite, quite out of the question," grunted Pink Pig. "I am too fat to go anywhere."

"I suppose 'out of the question' means 'No'," said Little Red Hen. "I will take it myself."

And she did. She went to the baker and brought back a crusty loaf.

"Who will help me eat this lovely new bread?" she clucked.

The animals all gathered around.

"I will!" said Ginger Cat, twitching his whiskers.

"So will I!" squeaked Grey Rat. "I am so hungry."

"Don't forget me!" grunted Pink Pig. "It looks delicious!"

"It is delicious," said Little Red Hen, "but you didn't help me at all . . . so it is quite out of the question for you to have any of it! Cluck! Cluck!"

143

The cock crows in the morn
To tell us to rise,
And he that lies late
Will never be wise:
For early to bed,
And early to rise,
Is the way to be healthy
And wealthy and wise.

Dance to your daddy,
My little babby,
Dance to your daddy, my little lamb;
You shall have a fishy
In a little dishy,
You shall have a fishy when the boat comes in.

144

Dickery, dickery, dare,
The pig flew up in the air;
The man in brown soon brought him down,
Dickery, dickery, dare.

Curly locks, Curly locks,
Wilt thou be mine?
Thou shalt not wash dishes
Nor yet feed the swine,
But sit on a cushion
And sew a fine seam,
And feed upon strawberries,
Sugar and cream.

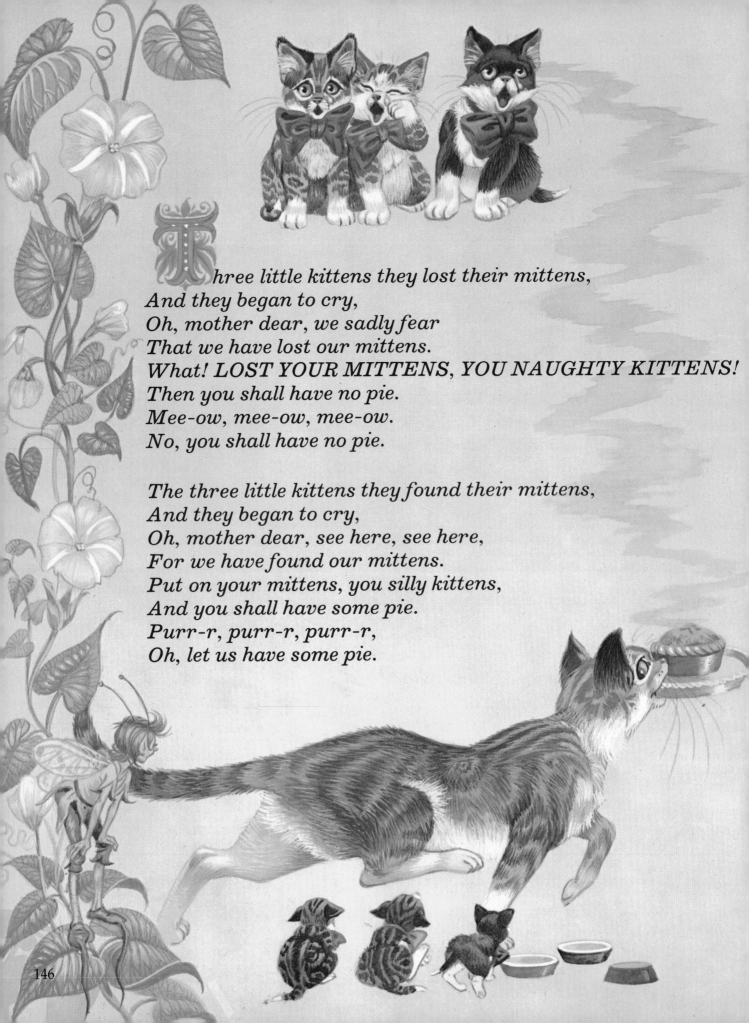

Three little kittens they lost their mittens,
And they began to cry,
Oh, mother dear, we sadly fear
That we have lost our mittens.
What! LOST YOUR MITTENS, YOU NAUGHTY KITTENS!
Then you shall have no pie.
Mee-ow, mee-ow, mee-ow.
No, you shall have no pie.

The three little kittens they found their mittens,
And they began to cry,
Oh, mother dear, see here, see here,
For we have found our mittens.
Put on your mittens, you silly kittens,
And you shall have some pie.
Purr-r, purr-r, purr-r,
Oh, let us have some pie.

The three little kittens put on their mittens,
And soon ate up the pie;
Oh, mother dear, we greatly fear
That we have soiled our mittens.
What! soiled your mittens, you naughty kittens!
Then they began to sigh.
Mee-ow, mee-ow, mee-ow.
Then they began to sigh.

The three little kittens they washed their mittens,
And hung them out to dry;
Oh! mother dear, do you not hear
That we have washed our mittens?
What! washed your mittens, then you're good kittens,
But I smell a rat close by.
Mee-ow, mee-ow, mee-ow.
We smell a rat close by.

Oh, the brave old Duke of York,
He had ten thousand men;
He marched them up to the top of the hill,
And he marched them down again.
And when they were up, they were up,
And when they were down, they were down,
And when they were only half-way up,
They were neither up nor down.

148

Bye, baby bunting,
Daddy's gone a-hunting,
Gone to get a rabbit skin
To wrap the baby bunting in.

149

The Three Little Pigs

Once upon a time there were three little pigs who lived together in one house. As they grew bigger their house seemed to grow smaller, and one day they decided to build three separate houses.

The first little pig built himself a house of straw.

The second little pig built himself a house of sticks.

The third little pig built himself a house of bricks.

The house of bricks took much longer to build than the other two, but it was the strongest when it was finished.

Soon after the first little pig had moved into his house there was a knock at the door.

"Little pig, little pig let me come in," said the wily old wolf, thinking how nice it would be to have pig for dinner.

"No, no, by the hair of my chinny chin chin, I will not let you in," said the first little pig.

"Then I'll huff, and I'll puff, and I'll blow your house in," growled the wolf.

And that is exactly what he did. The straw house blew

away in the wind and the wolf gobbled up the pig.

When the wolf saw the house built of sticks, he licked his lips and said:

"Little pig, little pig, let me come in."

"No, no, by the hair of my chinny chin chin, I will not let you in," said the second little pig.

"Then I'll huff, and I'll puff, and I'll blow your house in," growled the wolf.

The house of sticks was as easy to blow down as the house of straw, and that was the end of the second little pig.

The wolf knew there was a third little pig about somewhere and when he saw the house of bricks he called through the letter box.

"Let me in little pig."

"No, no, by the hair of my chinny chin chin, I will not let you in," said the third little pig.

"Then I'll huff and I'll puff and I'll blow your house in," said the wolf.

And the wolf huffed and he

puffed, and he puffed and he huffed, until he was quite out of breath, and still the house of bricks stood firm and secure. It didn't even creak.

"I can see I'll have to be rather clever to catch this little pig," said the wolf. "I'll have to lure him outside his house."

He told the little pig about a field he knew where the turnips were ready for digging, and arranged to meet him there next morning.

But the third little pig was

much cleverer than the wolf realised. He knew exactly what the wolf was up to. He had been to the field, dug up the turnips and was safely back indoors before the wolf had even woken up.

The wolf tried to keep his temper. He told the little pig about a tree he knew that was weighed down with juicy red apples.

"I'll meet you there in the morning," he said slyly.

The wolf wasn't going to be caught again and next day he

got up very early. When he reached the orchard the little pig was still in the tree picking apples.

"I'll throw you one," called the little pig, and he threw an apple so that it rolled into the long grass.

While the wolf was looking for it the little pig jumped from the tree and ran home. He was safely inside his brick house before the wolf realised he had been tricked.

By this time the wolf was getting very annoyed . . .

and hungry.

"I'll meet you at the fair tomorrow," he said.

The little pig did go to the fair next day. He bought himself a butter churn. He was on his way home when he caught sight of the wolf. As quick as a raindrop hiding in a puddle, he hid himself in the butter churn and began to roll down the hill. He rolled right over the wolf's foot and frightened him horribly. He was safely inside his brick house before the wolf stopped trembling.

When the wolf discovered who had been inside the butter churn he was very angry indeed. He was determined that the little pig should not escape again. He climbed on to the roof of the brick house and began to ease himself down the brick chimney.

The little pig was very frightened when he heard the wolf mumbling and grumbling inside his chimney, but he didn't panic. He built up the fire and set his biggest cooking pot on the flames.

The wolf slithered down the chimney and fell into the pot with an enormous splash and a very loud OUCH!!! And that, I am glad to say, was the end of the wolf.

I see the moon,
And the moon sees me;
God bless the moon,
And God bless me.

Twinkle, twinkle, little star,
How I wonder what you are!
Up above the world so high,
Like a diamond in the sky.

When the blazing sun is gone,
When he nothing shines upon,
Then you show your little light,
Twinkle, twinkle, all the night.

Then the traveller in the dark,
Thanks you for your tiny spark,
He could not see which way to go,
If you did not twinkle so.

In the dark blue sky you keep,
And often through my curtains peep,
For you never shut your eye,
'Till the sun is in the sky.

As your bright and tiny spark,
Lights the traveller in the dark,
Though I know not what you are,
Twinkle, twinkle, little star.